IDYL

JEFF JONES
IDYL

For the Allreds
Jeff Jones

DRAGON'S DREAM

A Dragon's Dream Book

Dragon's Dream,
Postbus 212,
3340 AE Hendrik-Ido-Ambacht,
Holland.

Sales: United Kingdom:
Big O Publishing,
219 Eversleigh Road,
London SW11 5UY,
England.
Telephone: 01-228 3392
Telex: 914 549

ISBN: 90 6332 671 8

Sales: United States:
Big O Publishing,
Box 6186,
Charlottesville VA 22906,
U.S.A.
Telephone: 804-977 3035
Telex: 822 438

ISBN: 90 6332 671 8

Printed in the Netherlands by Chevalier

This book is dedicated—
"To all but Entropy—
and especially to Mark Twain,
Don Marquis and Lewis Carroll."

Introduction

i dyl, i dyll (i'd'l), n. [L. idyllium; Gr. eidyllion, dim. of eidos, a form, figure, image].

Webster's New World Dictionary
of the American Language.

Jeff Jones is an artist of immeasurably rich gifts, and in 'Idyl' he has given us something that is very, very special.

A creation that exists concurrently on many different levels, it is, most immediately, a series of glimpses into a lush pastoral world of beautiful and moodily evocative landscapes. Populating this world is a cast of such diverse and highly unlikely characters as reasoning fish, talkative butterflies, contemplative leopards, turtles, and birds —and, to include two of my own personal favorites —a clam who relates the evolutionary history of his species, and a head-scratching, dourfully perplexed chimpanzee who struggles manfully to unravel the hopelessly confused threads of a paradox.

These —to list but a few —as well as a further assortment of personified flowers, bushes, and stones, readily engage in bouts of philosophic and metaphysical speculation, trading insights, double entendres, and their various points of view. An extraordinary sort of place, to say the least, and one peopled by no-less-extraordinary inhabitants.

Over it all presides the wistfully enigmatic central character of 'Idyl.' Newly-born (but not yesterday) and pregnant with thought), she moves dreamily through this world, giving it shape and illumination even as it shapes and illuminates her. Poised, aloof, and maintaining a somewhat ambivalent relationship to her surroundings, she still somehow seems to possess some inner knowledge of its mysterious laws; and it is with and through her that the work—as well as the world—begins to unfold and transcend its immediately apparent bounds.

For on other and entirely different levels, 'Idyl' intimates and manifests a wholly new spectrum of concerns. Word and pictures grow confused, their verbal and visual symbols interweaving and conjoining in swirling Joycean pastiche of thought. Linear and symbolic logic convolute; percept merges with concept; the line distinguishing image from meaning wavers, blurs, and falls away; subject commingles with object, freely flowing and evolving into a tapestry of new and further definitions of context, content, and form. And through the whole Jones has woven and scattered and constantly frames and reframes questions: motifs of time and existence, intuition, perception, experience, sleep and death.

'Idyl' is, as I have previously stated, something very very special. As one man's extremely personal vehicle of exploration and thought, it may sometimes leave us, like that aforementioned chimpanzee, scratching our heads in mute bewilderment, completely nonplussed. It almost always, however, succeeds in subtly altering the ways in which we perceive our own surroundings and—much more importantly—ourselves. For in the end, 'Idyl' offers no final or absolute answer, only new and ever-regenerative ways of thinking and feeling and seeing. So just what is Jones doing? He is re-inventing the word for world.

IDYL

IDYL

> YOU GOT AFFLICTIONS, WOMAN. YOU IS IN BAD SHAPE.

> I HAVE PLIED MY **MASCULINE** VIRTUES TO THE TASK.

> THESE **SPECTACLES** I INVENTED WILL CORRECT YOUR NARROW NEARSIGHTEDNESS...

> ...THROUGH THE POTENCY AND GENIUS OF THE PROGRESSIVE, AGGRESSIVE MALE ANIMAL...

> ...YOU WILL NOW BE ABLE TO TRANSCEND THE FRIVOLOUS **PRESENT** – TO SEE THE **LIGHT!**

SSSSSSSSSS CRACKLE

IDYL

IDYL

IDYL

MOMMY, WHAT DADDY'S DOING IN THE WOODS.

OH, HE'S JUST TRYING TO FIND **MEANING** TO HIS OWN EXISTANCE.

THINK I'LL **PISS** ON THAT TREE.

DAMN! NO MATTER HOW HARD YOU SHAKE **IT** THERE'S ALWAYS **ONE** DROP LEFT THAT ROLLS DOWN YOUR LEG.

I THINK HE'S **NEAT**.

YOU LOOK **UP** TO HIM. HE'S YOUR **IDOL**. THAT GIVES YOU **STRUCTURE**. HE HAS **NO ONE** TO LOOK UP TO.

BUT LAST WEEK HE INVENTED **GODS**. SO **NOW** HE CAN CLAIM TO BE MADE IN THEIR **IMAGE**. TO BE LIKE A **GOD**—THAT'S SOMETHING—THAT'S **MEANING**.

WITH THIS TALLEYWACKER I PISS ON THE **GODS**!

FAR OUT.

THE **GODS** WON'T LAST LONG THOUGH, HE WON'T BE ABLE TO **STAND** NOT **BEING** ONE **HIMSELF**.

I AM THE **LORD OF** THE UNIVERSE. **I ALONE** AM THE SHAPER OF. . .**GOD**! LOOK AT THAT, IT'S **DEAD**, JUST LYING THERE— AN **ANIMAL** ALL ROTTEN LIKE. A BIG, **STRONG** THING LIKE THAT. . .

BUT, MOMMY, HOW COME **YOU** AREN'T LOOKING FOR **MEANING** TO **LIFE**?

I DON'T NEED TO — I'VE **GOT** IT.

OH, **GOD**, I'M GONNA **DIE**!

I AM THE VESSEL, THE **BACKBONE** AND THE **STUFF** ITSELF.

MOTHER.

THE LONEWORN LADY

A MISOGYNIST MOON

OH, MY **GOD!**

THE END OF THE SPOON

STIRRING

OH! WHAT WILL HE **DO?** WHAT **WILL** HE DO?

THE WHITEPURE PROMISE— THE AMERICAN GOTHIC

A **FATE** WORSE THAN **DEATH!**

AH, THE MORNING SUN.

IT'S A **RESTLESS** LIFE WHEN YOU'RE **HAUNTED** BY YOUR **DREAMS.**

IDYL

$c = 2\pi r$

I DON'T KNOW WHERE I AM. COULD YOU HELP?

WELL, **FIRST** YOU HAVE TO HAVE A PLACE TO GO. WE'VE **ALL** GOT TO HAVE A PLACE TO GO.

THEN THE SHORTEST WAY THERE IS A **STRAIGHT** LINE — OR TO BE **PRECISE**, IN CURVED SPACE, IS A CURVED LINE.

YOU CAN FIGURE HOW **LONG** IT WILL TAKE YOU TO GET THERE. IN THE FORMULA **D = RT**, WHERE **D** IS THE DISTANCE AND...

BUT I DON'T KNOW **WHERE** I'M GOING.

OH... WELL A STRAIGHT LINE IS **STILL** SHORTEST.

AND YOU SHOULD **NEVER** FORGET THE **SQUARE-CUBE** LAW!... BUT I GUESS THAT DOESN'T APPLY HERE. SO YOU CAN FORGET THE **SQUARE-CUBE** LAW.

BUT I DON'T...

DOESN'T MATTER! YOU CAN GO **THIS** WAY OR **THAT** WAY OR **ANYWAY.** DOESN'T MATTER!

YOU'LL JUST END UP BACK **HERE** AGAIN, EVENTUALLY. **SO WHY GO?** YOU SEE, ON A SPHEROID ——

YOU'RE NOT MUCH HELP.

I THINK I'LL JUST WANDER AROUND.

TRY TO GIVE THEM AN OBJECT LESSON IN **SOLID GEOMETRY** AND THEY GET **TOPOLOGICAL** ON YOU.

IDYL

IDYL

IDYL

BUT **WHERE** DOES IT GET YOU?

SUBSTITUTES DON'T **RESOLVE** ANYTHING.

IT'S JUST A **REINFORCED** BEHAVIOR PATTERN.

FULFILLMENT IS LINEAR.

WHAT ARE YOU **REALLY** LOOKING FOR?

WE SHOULD **ALL** RID OURSELVES OF SUBSTITUTE PATTERNS.

LISTEN, I'M TIRED. I WANT TO GET SOME SLEEP.

BLAM

IDYL

ARIS- TOTLE

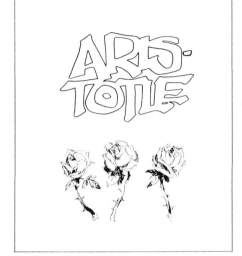

BARRELS!

I WONDER IF THERE'S ANYTHING **IN THEM**.

NOTHING IN **THIS** ONE.

IDYL

I STAND ACCUSED, YOU UNDERSTAND...

...OF ALL.

OF RAPING VACUUM-SEALED VIRGIN MARY. MADNESS.

OF GLUTTONY ABOVE THE KNEES, AND OF SPILLING THE BEANS.

BUT I CAN NEVER GET THESE BOOTS ON UNTIL I'VE WORN THEM FOR AWHILE.

THOUGH I STAND IN NEUTRAL, CHOSEN, IDYL, AND UNAFRAID, I FEED MYSELF, LET OTHERS FEED THE HORSE. I TOOK SO MUCH MEDICINE I WAS SICK A LONG TIME AFTER I GOT WELL.

THE HILLS DON'T GET ANY HIGHER, THE VALLEYS GET DEEPER. YOU TELL ME, WHAT GOES THROUGH FIRST— THE BULLET OR THE HOLE?

IF ONE OF US MUST KILL THE OTHER—LET IT BE ME.

SELL THE HIDE AFTER YOU'VE KILLED THE BUFFALO.

A STITCH IN TIME SAVES NINE.

?

I'M JUST TRYING TO SEE HOW MUCH THEY'LL SWALLOW BEFORE THEY ASK FOR A DOUGHNUT.

IDYL

IDYL

WHAT ARE YOU **DOING**?

I'M GOING TO **PUNCH** MY HEAD OUT.

WHY'RE YOU GOING TO DO **THAT**?

BECAUSE THERE'S NOTHING **ELSE** TO DO. I ALREADY DID IT ALL.

I SHOOK HANDS WITH THE PRESIDENT AND KISSED THE KING'S **ASS**. I MET A FRIENDLY **INDIAN**.

AND LAID A **BIVALVE**.

I WENT TO **WALES** AND SAW A **DUCK**. I ATE CROW AND I LET A GIANT STEP IN MY **BUCKET**.

BUT THAT'S NOT **EVERYTHING**!

NOT QUITE. I NEVER **PUNCHED** MY HEAD OUT.

YOU COULD...

...PICK FLOWERS.

IDYL

BEHOLD. A BIRD OF PREY. AWAKE, AWING, AND AWANT. A NOT **TOO**, **TOO** UNUSUAL SIGHT.

AHHH! BUT, **NOW**, BEHOLD A HORMONE REFRAIN, CLAD ONLY IN **BRA** AND **PANTIES**.

WELL, SHE SANG A SONG **SWEETLY**, SO :

WHILE THE BIRD SOARED.

AND AS FATE WOULD HAVE IT. . .

SHE TOOK OFF HER **BRA** AND **PANTIES**.

AND THE BIRD. . . WELL, HE JUST SOARED.

THE BIRD, NOW, WHEN HE SIGHTED THE GIRL WITHOUT THE **BRA** AND **PANTIES** . . .

. . .WELL, HE JUST SOARED.

IDYL

IDYL

IDYL

IDYL

IDYL
IN
EXCESS

I WAS BORN JUST THIS MORNING.

I LEARN FAST. THAT'S BECAUSE I NOTICE THINGS.

JUST A WHILE AGO, WHILE I WAS NOTICING SOMETHING OR OTHER, IT BEGAN TO RAIN.

WELL, I HAD BEEN SO BUSY NOTICING THINGS, THAT IT JUST SORT OF SNEAKED UP ON ME.

I BEGAN TO THINK WHAT TO DO.

I DECIDED THAT ONE AS EDUCATED AS I SHOULD KNOW ENOUGH TO GET OUT OF THE RAIN.

SO I RAN VERY FAST AND JUMPED INTO THE LAKE.

THAT WAS TERRIBLY CLEVER, I THINK, FOR ONE SO YOUNG.

I WASN'T BORN YESTERDAY.

IDYL

I'M DOING ART.

I'M DOING AN ELEPHANT.

WHAT'S ART?

ART'S WHEN YOU DO SOMETHING WITH UNUSUAL PERCEPTION. I'M UNUSUALLY PERCEPTIVE.

WHAT KIND OF ART ARE YOU DOING?

ETCHING. I'M STARING RIGHT AT THE SUN AND MOVING MY EYES WITH UNUSUAL PERCEPTION.

IS THAT ART?

I'M ETCHING AN ELEPHANT ON MY LEFT RETINA.

IDYL

WHEN I DIE I'D LIKE TO COME BACK AS A BEAUTIFUL, DIAPHANOUS, **MOTH.**

I'D BE GLORY PERSONIFIED, RIDING HIGH ALONG THE COOL, NIGHTTIME BREEZE.

LIVING ONLY FOR **PURPOSE** AND **LIGHT.**

TRYING TO FORGET WHEN I WAS A **CATERPILLAR.**

I'D LIVE ALOFT, PASSIONATELY, DESPERATELY...

SEARCHING FOR A **FLAME** TO LEAP INTO.

MAYBE I'D RATHER COME BACK AS A **SPONGE.**

I TALK MORE THAN MOST.

IT'S BECAUSE I WANT TO BE SURE TO SAY WHAT I MEAN BEFORE I'M FINISHED.

I WAS TALKING TO A PARAMECIUM ABOUT EVOLUTION...

...AND THE INJUSTICE OF SIZE.

HE TOLD ME THAT IF GORILLAS HAD BEEN THE SIZE OF PARAMECIUMS THEY'D NEVER HAVE BEEN ABLE TO PICK UP A HAMMER.

I WAS ABOUT TO TELL HIM THAT IF PARAMECIUMS HAD BEEN THE SIZE OF GORILLAS THEY'D PROBABLY HAVE BEEN GORILLAS...

...WHEN A BIG MOLECULE MASHED HIM.

IDYL

WHEN **HE** WAS BORN, MANY ENVIED HIS **POSITION**.

AS A BABY, MANY ENVIED HIS **CURDS**.

AS **HE** GREW, MANY ENVIED HIS **AMBITION**.

WHEN **HE** ELIMINATED, MANY ENVIED HIS **TURDS**.

WHEN **HE** ATE, MANY ENVIED HIS **DIGESTION**.

WHEN **HE** COPULATED,

MANY ENVIED HIS **BIRDS**.

WHEN **HE** GOT SICK, MANY ENVIED HIS **PHYSICIAN**.

WHEN **HE** SPOKE, MANY ENVIED HIS **WORDS**.

AND WHEN **HE** DIED, MANY ENVIED HIS **FUNERAL**.

IDYL

IDYL

I MET A VERY CLEVER ROCK WHOSE GREATEST AMBITION WAS TO BE ALIVE SO HE COULD LEAVE BEHIND A LOT OF LITTLE ROCKS.

HE TRIED MANY THINGS.

HE TOLD A FROG HE WOULD LOVE MOST TO BE A FROG SO HE COULD EAT ROCKS.

THE FROG DID AND NEVER MOVED AGAIN.

HE TOLD A BIRD HE WOULD LOVE MOST TO BE A BIRD SO HE COULD HATCH ROCKS.

THE BIRD TRIED AND NEVER MOVED AGAIN.

HE TOLD ME HE WOULD LOVE MOST TO BE HUMAN SO HE COULD TALK TO ROCKS.

I SMASHED HIM TO BITS WITH ANOTHER ROCK.

IDYL

IDYL FINDS A PHOBIA

LOST . . .

I SURE HOPE I DON'T BUMP INTO ONE.

I'M ABSOLUTELY TERRIFIED OF THEM.

OF A CERTAINTY, SOMETIMES SOUNDS IN THE SHADOWS CAN BE MOST ALLUSIVE.

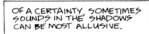
FINGERS.

MAYBE THAT'S ONE, NOW.

IEEEE! AAIII! GASP!
FINGERS!

YOU GOT FINGERS.

ARE YOU ONE?
WE'RE JUST A BUNCH OF FOUR FLOWERS.
I'VE NEVER SEEN A FOUR-FLOWER.

YOU ALL LOOK EXACTLY THE SAME!

IF WE WERE EXACTLY THE SAME, WE'D ALL BE ME.
ME
ME
PTTO!

BUT THEIR THOUGHTS WERE NOT LONG ON PHILOSOPHICAL TRUTHS. NOR WERE THEIR LIVES OFTEN GIVEN TO GREAT MIRTH.

FINGERS

FINGERS HA. HA. FIN-GERS

FINGERST

IT'S AWFUL DARK OUT THERE.

I REALLY MUST KEEP MOVING. THEY'RE ALL AROUND, I KNOW.

ALSO, SINCE OUR SPACE IS RUNNING OUT, AND WE'RE NOT AT ALL CONCERNED WITH FOUR FLOWERS, WE HAD BEST BACK UP AND CONTINUE, RESOLVING OUR STORY AS IF THEY HAD NEVER HAPPENED.

MAYBE THAT'S ONE, NOW.

IDYL

IDYL IS SOUGHT OUT BY A SMALL TREE TO TALK ABOUT IMPORTANT THINGS LIKE **MATHEMATICS**.

MATHEMATICS.

I WATCHED IT FOR **THREE** DAYS AND IT NEVER FLAPPED ONCE.

AO CACHCHCH.

I SEE...

AHEM! OH, I SEE. YES! YES! MUST REMAIN UNFLAPPABLE.

IT FLAPPED EVENTUALLY.

IT FLAPS? THEN. SOMETIMES.

MOST OF THE TIME.

SO.

IDYL IS SOUGHT OUT BY A LARGE ROCK TO TALK ABOUT IMPORTANT THINGS LIKE **ART**.

IDYL IS SOUGHT OUT BY A **VERY** LARGE ROCK TO CHANGE THE SUBJECT.

ART.

IT HAD SUCH VITALITY AND WAS QUITE HIGH BLOWN ONCE. BUT THEN IT PLUMMETED BECAUSE IT DIDN'T FLAP.

UH....

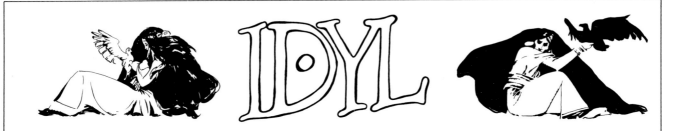

IDYL, IN HER MEANDERING, STUMBLES UPON THE BLOCK, THE **HINGED STONE**.

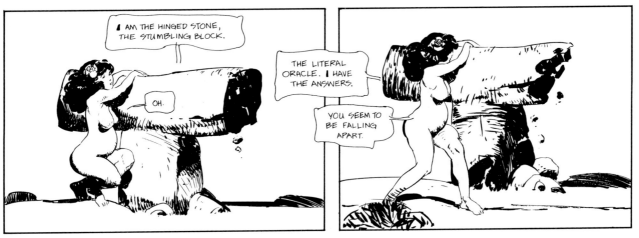

THERE IS A LENGTHY PAUSE OF WARY DESCENT.   WE SHALL BEGIN ANOTHER STORY.

IDYL

IT'LL BE **DARK** SOON.

I THINK IT'S ABSURD THAT **CIVILIZED** CREATURES LIKE OURSELVES HAVE TO FALL DOWN **UNCONSCIOUS** EVERY TIME IT GETS **DARK**.

I MEAN, HERE WE ARE SPEAKING ON ENLIGHTENED SUBJECTS LIKE 'WHY?' AND IF IT SUDDENLY GOT **DARK** AND WE FELL DOWN **UNCONSCIOUS** EVERYTHING WOULD HAVE TO STOP.

WE BETTER START LOOKING FOR A PLACE TO **SLEEP**.

I HAD A BROTHER WHO LAST YEAR DECIDED HE WAS THROUGH WITH **SLEEP**. HE STUMBLED INTELLECTUALLY OUT ONE VERY **DARK** NIGHT TO PICK SOME BANANAS.

AND STAGGERED OFF A **CLIFF**.

IT'LL BE **DARK** SOON. WE BETTER START LOOKING FOR A PLACE TO **SLEEP**

IDYL

ONCE UPON A TIME THERE WERE THESE THINGS.

THERE WAS LOTS OF STUFF THEY COULD DO AND LOTS THEY COULDN'T DO.

THEY COULDN'T **SMELL** BECAUSE THEY DIDN'T HAVE ANY HEADS.

WHAT ABOUT NOSES?

NO HEADS?

THEY COULDN'T **HEAR** BECAUSE...

...THEY DIDN'T HAVE ANY HEADS?

NO! BECAUSE THERE WASN'T ANY NOISE.

THEY COULDN'T **SEE** BECAUSE...

...THEY STUFFED DUCKS IN THEIR EYES!

DO YOU WANT TO HEAR MY STORY?

YES.

...BECAUSE THEY NEVER WOKE UP.

THEY COULDN'T TASTE BECAUSE THEY NEVER ATE.

AND THEY COULDN'T FEEL BECAUSE...

...THEY STARVED TO DEATH IN THEIR SLEEP.

AHEM.

WHAT **COULD** THEY DO?

IDYL

THERE WE WERE THERE WALKING OUT ALONG MY FAVORITE CLIFF WHEN I ASKED HAVE YOU LATELY OR EVEN EVER FOR THAT MATTER BEEN SOMETHING ELSE AS HE MUTTERED SOMETHING STRANGE ABOUT AN UNIMPORTANT STAR HE SEEMED OVERWHELMINGLY PREOCCUPIED WITH SO MY QUESTION WAS CUT AS HE POINTED TO HIS FINGERS ONE BY ONE WHILE I KEPT CHECKING TO SEE IF I HADN'T LOST A FOOT SOMEWHERE ALONG THE WAY. I NEVER DID KNOW ONE TO COME OFF THE LEG YOU KNOW AND HE DARE I MENTION MY CONCERN WOULD CERTAINLY RAVE ABOUT INDUCTION OR PROBABILITIES OR SOMETHING ELSE TERRIBLY INVENTIVE AND IRRELEVANT SAYING ALSO ALL THE WHILE THAT FEET ARE FEET AND DON'T COME OFF. WHILE HE TALKED I ASKED JUST TO SAY A THING AM I SPELLING THINGS CORRECTLY TO AVOID THE SUBJECT OF MY FEET WHICH I DIDN'T ANYHOW WANT TO TALK ABOUT SO AS TO OFFEND SOME SIMPLE CERTAINTY OF HIS BUT HE JUST LOOKED AT ME BLANK. SO I CHANGED THE SUBJECT WHILE THE SEA BEAT BELOW ACROSS THE SAND AND ASKED HIM ABOUT HIS STAR WHICH TO MY SURPRISE TURNED OUT TO BE THE SUN. IMAGINE JUST IMAGINE! HIS FINGERS FLEW AS HE RAVED ABOUT. I DIDN'T WANT TO ASK IF HE WAS LOONEY BECAUSE HE SEEMED SO POINTEDLY UNBALANCED. TWO TRILLION HE SAID HOLDING UP TWO TRILLION FINGERS. ONE. TWO. I CHECKED MY LEFT FOOT AGAIN CAUTIOUSLY SO HE WOULDN'T NOTICE. THAT THE SUN THERE HE POINTED WITH ONE TRILLION FINGERS HAD COME UP TWO TRILLION TIMES AND HE WAS AFRAID THAT IT MIGHT NEVER COME UP AGAIN. IMAGINE! HE MUMBLED THAT THE ODDS OF SOMETHING SLIGHTLY LESS THAN TWO TRILLION TO ONE OF IT EVER NOT COMING UP AGAIN WEREN'T EVEN GOOD ENOUGH TO GET TO SLEEP AT NIGHT DARTING APPREHENSIVE GLANCES NOW AND THEN TOWARD THE MOST WONDERFUL SUNSET AND WELL I CERTAINLY DIDN'T WANT TO STEP ON ALL HIS CAREFUL PROBABILITIES AND STATISTICS SO I TOLD HIM WITH A QUICK GLANCE AT MY FEET THAT IT WOULD EITHER COME UP OR IT WOULDN'T. YOU KNOW. NOT TO WORRY ABOUT BEFORE OR ABOUT HIS FINGERS. IT HAD JUST AS GOOD A CHANCE OF COMING UP AS NOT. EVEN ODDS FIFTY-FIFTY HE MIGHT HAVE SAID IF HE HADN'T WALKED RIGHT OFF THE CLIFF RIGHT THEN AND WITHOUT EVEN SCREAMING TOO. ON THINKING LATER I SUPPOSE IT MIGHT COME HALF-WAY UP AND IF HE HAD WAITED I COULD HAVE TOLD HIM THAT TOO. I SHOULD HAVE THOUGHT OF THAT SOONER I GUESS BUT I WAS OCCUPIED FOR A WHILE WITH MY RIGHT ANKLE WHICH HAD SUSPICIOUSLY DISAPPEARED INTO SOME TALL GRASS.